JOURNEYS

Standards-Based Assessment Resource

Kindergarten

Houghton
Mifflin
Harcourt

Contents

Overview

Assessments and Performance Tasks

As you use the Houghton Mifflin Harcourt *Journeys* instructional program, you have a rich array of materials to foster children's achievement week by week and unit by unit. The *Standards-Based Assessment Resource* includes Assessments and Performance Tasks that align with the content in *Journeys* and give children practice with the high-stakes tests they will encounter. Rigorous tasks and questions, complex text, and technology-enhanced item formats (online only) prepare children for success on standards-based assessments. At the end of each unit, you can use an Assessment or Performance Task to obtain a broader picture of achievement.

Assessments

The Assessments can be given three times a year, at the end of Units 1, 3, and 5. These tests are cumulative. The Unit 1 Assessment draws from Unit 1, while the Units 3 and 5 Assessments draw upon skills that have been taught in the current and previous units. The item types and assessment formats presented are the same kinds that children will encounter on high-stakes tests and provide essential practice in test-taking strategies.

Each Assessment has four sections. The Reading section assesses comprehension and vocabulary strategies. The Writing section draws upon the grammar, spelling, and writing skills taught to date. The Listening section presents audio or read-aloud passages that assess the listening skills that children will encounter on high-stakes tests. The Research section assesses a combination of comprehension, research/media literacy, and writing skills.

The Listening section of the Assessments includes a source that children must listen to and then answer questions about. The source will not be available as text to children. If you administer a paper-and-pencil version of the Assessments, you will read the source aloud to children. If you administer the online Assessment, children will need to access audio on a computer.

Performance Tasks

The Performance Tasks can also be given three times a year, at the end of Units 2, 4, and 6. Each Performance Task draws upon the reading, writing, and research skills taught in the current and previous units. These tasks encourage children to integrate knowledge and skills to conduct complex analysis and research.

A brief Classroom Activity will be conducted prior to each Performance Task to orient children to the context of the task. The Classroom Activity includes a summary of one source from the Performance Task and prompts for a classroom discussion. At the end of the Classroom Activity, the teacher will be directed to make a brief statement that explains the purpose of the activity within the context of the Performance Task as a whole.

Each Performance Task features two parts. Part 1 introduces a group of related text sources. Children should be encouraged to take notes as they read the sources. After the sources, children will encounter a set of questions related to the passage. The answers to the items will be scored. Part 2 introduces the essay prompt, along with a brief description of the scoring criteria. The essay will be scored using one of three rubrics.

A Note About Previewing Words

The texts in both the Assessments and the Performance Tasks may have some words that are not readable to young children. These words have been identified for previewing in the Guidelines for Administering. Other portions of the text are composed of pictures, fully-decodable words, and high-frequency words. When previewing words with children, follow this routine: Write the words on the board and read them for children. For each word, say, "This **word** is in your story or article today. It is **word**. Say it with me: **word**."

General Guidelines for Administering

The Assessments and Performance Tasks are group-administered and may be taken online or as a paper-and-pencil version. At Kindergarten and Grade 1, some sections of the tests are read aloud. These sections are noted in the specific guidelines for administering the tests. At Grade 2 and beyond, children can read the directions and take the tests independently. At all grades, the Listening section of the Assessments and the Classroom Activity of the Performance Tasks will be administered by the teacher.

Test Time

The Assessments are not timed. The Performance Tasks have suggested completion times listed on the teacher overview pages.

Allowable Resources

Children may access several resources while they complete the Assessments and Performance Tasks.

> **Pen/pencil/highlighter and blank/lined paper:** Children are encouraged to take notes throughout the Performance Tasks, and they may choose to take notes as they complete the Assessments.

> **Hard-copy dictionary:** Children are allowed to access dictionaries as they write the essay during Part 2 of the Performance Task.

> **Headphones:** All children will need headphones to complete the Listening section of each online Assessment.

Item Types

The Assessments and the Performance Tasks include the following item types:

- Selected-response items: These multiple-choice items require children to choose an answer from several provided options. Some items will require children to select multiple correct options. Children should circle or draw an X through their answer choices.

- Constructed-response items: These items require children to write or type a response.

- Interactive items: Interactive items require children to complete a table or underline a portion of the text. Interactive items online require children to interact with the text by clicking cells in a table or highlighting a portion of text.

Guidelines for Administering Assessment 1

Use the following directions as you administer each section.

Writing

Say: *A student wrote this story. Look at the pictures and listen carefully as I read the story. You will answer questions about the story afterward.*

I Like the Park

I like the leaves. I like the birds. I like the dogs. I like the owls.

Item 1: Say: *Draw something that you like at the park. Then write about your picture.*

Listening

The Listening prompts are below for read-aloud presentation.

Say: *Look at the pictures and listen carefully as I read the article. You will answer questions about the article afterward.*

Amazing Spiders

Did you know that spiders are not insects? Insects have six legs. Spiders have eight legs. All spiders have long, sharp teeth called fangs.

There are many kinds of spiders. Spiders can be big or small. The Goliath bird-eating tarantula is bigger than your hand.

Spiders help people. They eat bugs that harm farmers' crops. They also eat mosquitoes and cockroaches. Both of these insects can make people sick. Some spiders spin strong silk webs to catch insects. Spiders are amazing!

Directions for items 2–4 follow. Help children identify the pictures or words in each row if necessary.

Item 2: Say: *How many legs does a spider have?*

two

four

eight

Item 3: Say: *What are **two** things that you learned from the article?*

Spiders eat bugs.

Spiders can harm crops.

Spiders can be big or small.

Item 4: Say: *Which detail that you heard from the article tells about how spiders are amazing?*

Insects have six legs.

Spiders can be big or small.

Some spiders spin strong silk webs to catch insects.

Say: *Look at the pictures and listen carefully as I read the story. You will answer questions about the story afterward.*

What Are Insects Good For?

We went to the park. We had a picnic. Johnny wanted to play on the swings. He heard a bee. Bees can sting.

Johnny ran. He fell in a mud puddle. The bee flew away. "Bugs are bad news!" Johnny said. I told Johnny that bugs are not all bad.

Insects make things. Bees make honey. "What other insects make things?" asked Johnny. I told him that silkworms make silk. Insects are good!

Directions for items 5–7 follow. Help children identify the pictures or words in each row if necessary.

Item 5: Say: *Why does Johnny run from the bee?*

He likes bees.

He is afraid of it.

He wants to play a game.

Item 6: Say: *What is the story mostly about?*

Bugs are bad news.

Insects can help.

Bees can sting.

Item 7: Say: *Which **two** details from the story tell about how some bugs are good?*

Bees can sting.

Silkworms make silk.

Bees make honey.

Guidelines for Administering Performance Task 1

Helping Others

Classroom Activity *(10 minutes)*

1. Tell children that you will read an article about ways people help others. Then read the following article aloud slowly.

Everyone Can Help

People can help do many things. A doctor can help a sick person get well. A dentist can clean our teeth so they will stay healthy. A teacher can help children learn.

You don't have to have an important job to help people. Kids can help people, too. A boy can help his dad in the kitchen. A girl can help walk the dog.

Everyone can help! Helping is fun!

2. Lead a brief class discussion about the article, using the questions below.

   Question 1: How can a doctor help people?

   Question 2: How can kids help people?

   Question 3: How have people helped you?

3. Explain to children that they will use this article and another article to draw and write a story about a time they helped someone.

Student Task Overview

Part 1 *(10 minutes)*

Tell children that you will read an article about trucks. Then read the following article aloud slowly.

Trucks

Trucks help people do lots of jobs. A garbage truck helps get rid of trash that people throw out. Trash collectors pick up garbage and take it to a dump.

A fire truck helps put out fires. It has ladders and hoses that firefighters use to put out fires.

The directions for each item are below. Help children identify the pictures in each row as best as they can. Reread the articles aloud multiple times if needed.

Item 1: Say: *Listen to the question about "Everyone Can Help": Which person helps a sick person get well?*

Item 2: Say: *Listen to the question about "Trucks": What is the article mostly about?*

Part 2 *(15 minutes)*

Tell children that they will now draw a picture and write a story. Read both articles again. Then read the following prompt aloud slowly: *Think about the information in the two articles, "Everyone Can Help" and "Trucks." How have you helped someone in a similar way to what you heard in the articles? Draw a picture to tell a story about a time when you helped someone like that. Then write to tell about it.*

Task Specifications and Scoring Rubrics

Tell children that a good response is clear and responds to the prompt.

Ask children to verbally explain their drawings or elaborate on their writing. Take these verbal responses into account as you score children's responses using the Performance Task: Narrative Writing Rubric.

Guidelines for Administering Assessment 2

Use the following directions as you administer each section.

Writing

Say: *A student wrote this article. Look at the pictures and listen carefully as I read the article. You will answer a question about the article afterward.*

What Can You See in a City?

We can see a bridge. We can see a fire truck. We can see a stoplight. We can see a clock. We can see a building. We can see a stop sign.

Item 1: Say: *Draw something that you can see in a city. Then write about your picture.*

Listening

The Listening prompts below are for read-aloud presentation.

Say: *Look at the pictures and listen carefully as I read the article. You will answer questions about the article afterward.*

What Makes a Snowflake

What is a snowflake made of? Water in a cloud gets cold. It turns into bits of ice. The ice grows around dust in a cloud. The little bits stick together. They make icy shapes.

The icy shapes get heavy. They fall to the ground. The icy shapes are snowflakes! If it's too warm, they melt. If it's cold enough, they make snow!

No two snowflakes have the same shape. Some are round. Some are pointed. Some look like stars. Every snowflake is different!

Directions for items 2–4 follow. Help children identify the pictures or words in each row if necessary.

Item 2: Say: *Where do snowflakes come from?*

the ground

the sun

clouds

Item 3: Say: *What do some snowflakes look like?*

triangles

stars

squares

Item 4: Say: *How would the weather **most likely** feel like if you saw a snowflake?*

cold

hot

wet

Say: *Look at the pictures and listen carefully as I read the article. You will answer questions about the article afterward.*

Winter Fun

Do you like winter? In the winter the days are short. It stays dark longer. We do not have as much time to play outside.

Winter is cold. Cold air can bring snow. It snows when drops of water in the clouds freeze. The icy snowflakes fall to the ground.

There are many things to do in the winter. We can build a snowman. We can go sledding. We can throw snowballs. We can make snow angels. Winter is fun!

Directions for items 5–7 follow. Help children identify the pictures or words in each row if necessary.

Item 5: Say: *Why is there not much time to play outside in the winter?*

Winter is cold.

The days are short.

Cold air can bring snow.

Item 6: Say: *What are* **two** *details from the article that support the main idea?*

It stays dark longer.

We can go sledding.

We can build a snowman.

Item 7: Say: *What is one conclusion you can draw about how the author feels about winter?*

She does not like the cold.

She likes to play in the snow.

She likes the short days of winter.

T12

Guidelines for Administering Performance Task 2

Animals and Insects

Classroom Activity *(10 minutes)*

1. Tell children that you will read an article about different kinds of bugs. Then read the following article aloud slowly.

Bugs, Bugs, Bugs

An insect has wings that help it fly.

A butterfly will use its wings to fly from flower to flower. It will drink nectar from a flower. Nectar is food for a butterfly.

A bee will flap its wings very fast to fly from flower to flower. This is what makes the buzzing sound that a bee makes.

A dragonfly uses its wings to fly back and forth very quickly. A dragonfly will catch and eat an insect as it flies.

2. Lead a brief class discussion about the article, using the questions below.

   Question 1: What sound does a bee make?

   Question 2: How are wings helpful to a butterfly?

3. Explain to children that they will use this article and another article to draw and write a report about creatures with wings.

Student Task Overview

Part 1 *(10 minutes)*

Tell children that you will read an article about birds. Then read the following article aloud slowly.

Feathered Friends

All birds have wings, feathers, and beaks. A hummingbird and an eagle use their wings to help them fly.

A hummingbird is tiny. It can be as tiny as a large insect. A hummingbird will flap its wings very fast. It can stay in the same place in the air while it drinks nectar from a flower.

An eagle is a very big bird. An eagle will use its big wings to fly way up high. It swoops down and catches food in its sharp claws.

Directions for item 1 are below. Use similar directions for item 2, changing *pictures* to *words* as appropriate. Help children identify the pictures in each row as best as they can. Read the article aloud multiple times if needed.

Item 1: Say: *Listen to the question about the article "Bugs, Bugs, Bugs": Which insect eats other bugs?*

butterfly

dragonfly

bee

Item 2: Say: *Look back at the picture of the hummingbird and listen to the question: What does the hummingbird use to drink nectar from flowers?*

beak

wing

feather

Part 2 *(15 minutes)*

Tell children they will now draw a picture and write a report. Read both articles again. Then read the following question aloud slowly: *Think about the information in the two articles I read, "Bugs, Bugs, Bugs" and "Feathered Friends." Do you think some creatures need their wings to find food?*

Task Specifications and Scoring Rubrics

Tell children that a good response is clear and answers the question.

Ask children to verbally explain their drawings or elaborate on their writing. Take these verbal responses into account as you score children's responses using the Performance Task: Opinion Writing Rubric.

Guidelines for Administering Assessment 3

Use the following directions as you administer each section.

Reading

We Can Help

Read the article title, directions, and items with children. The article should be read independently by children. Preview the following words before children read the article: *help, fun, ball.*

Directions for items 1 and 2 follow. Help children identify the pictures or words in each row if necessary.

Item 1: Say: *What can kids do after they help?*

help Pam go

jog with a dog

play with a pal

Item 2: Say: *Which word from the story tells how the author feels about helping? Underline the word.*

We can all help. Then we can play with a pal. It is good to help!

We Go to School

Read the article title, directions, and items with children. The article should be read independently by children. Preview the following words before children read the article: *fun, help, food.*

Directions for items 3–5 follow. Help children identify the pictures or words in each row if necessary.

Item 3: Say: *What do the children do first?*

They go.

They sit.

They play.

Item 4: Say: *Who do the children help with food?*

pets

kids

the man

Item 5: Say: *What does the man do at the end of the day? Draw a picture. Then write about your picture.*

The Tree

Read the story title, directions, and items with children. The story should be read independently by children. Preview the following words before children read the story: *tree, help, plums*.

Directions for items 6–8 follow. Help children identify the pictures or words in each row if necessary.

Item 6: Say: *Why is Tom happy?*

He got a tree.

They dig and dig.

The tree is not in the pot.

Item 7: Say: *What happens last in the story?*

We got plums.

The tree got big.

We put the tree in the pot.

Item 8: Say: *Look at the pictures. What does a tree need to grow?*

a flower

a plum

rain

Bob Dog and Pat Cat

Read the directions and items with children. The story should be read independently by children. Preview the following words before children read the story: *want, tree*.

Directions for items 9 and 10 follow. Help children identify the pictures or words in each row if necessary.

Item 9: Say: *Why does Bob Dog look up the tree?*

Pat is a dog.

Pat is up the tree.

He cannot see Pat.

Item 10: Say: *Which word from the story tells how Bob Dog felt at the beginning? Underline the word.*

Bob Dog was sad. I want to play. I see a cat!

Writing

Say: *A child wrote a journal. Look at the pictures and read the journal with me. You will answer a question about the journal afterward.*

What I Like

I can play a game. I like to play. It is fun!

I can go on a bus. I like to go on a bus. The bus is fun!

This is my big dog. She is a good dog! She is fun!

Item 11: Say: *Draw something that you think is fun. Then write about your picture.*

Listening

The Listening prompts are below for read-aloud presentation.

Say: *Look at the picture and listen carefully as I read the article. You will answer questions about the article afterward.*

Moon Shapes

The moon looks different each night. The moon can look like it is cut in half. This is called a half-moon. The moon can look like a banana. This is called a crescent moon. The moon shapes are called moon phases.

The shape of the moon does not change. The moon is always round. The moon goes around Earth. We see different parts of the moon lit up by the sun.

Directions for items 12–14 follow. Help children identify the pictures or words in each row if necessary.

Item 12: Say: *What is the article mostly about?*

the sun

Earth

the moon

Item 13: Say: *What does the moon go around?*

a wheel

Earth

the moon

Item 14: Say: *The moon looks different each night. What are two shapes that show how the moon can look?*

half-circle

square

crescent

Say: *Look at the pictures and listen carefully as I read the article. You will answer questions about the article afterward.*

Summer

Summer is a great season. You can play outside, but you also need to be safe.

Summer can get warm. The sun comes out and makes it hot. When it gets hot, you need to stay cool. Drink lots of water to be safe. Sometimes you can go swimming!

Summer can get wet, too. Clouds fill the sky, and it rains. You can play in the rain and splash in puddles. Sometimes there is thunder and lightning. Lightning can be dangerous. Go inside your house to be safe if you hear thunder.

Summer is fun! There is a lot to do.

Directions for items 15–17 follow. Help children identify the pictures or words in each row if necessary.

Item 15: Say: *What makes it hot in the summer?*

clouds

the sun

a house

Item 16: Say: *What two details from the article show how you can be safe in summer?*

drink water

play in puddles

go inside when there is thunder

Item 17: Say: *One conclusion you can draw is that when you hear thunder, it is not safe outside. Which detail from the article supports this idea?*

Lightning can be dangerous.

You can go swimming.

Drink water.

Guidelines for Administering Performance Task 3

High in the Sky

Classroom Activity *(20 minutes)*

1. Tell children that you will read an article about the sky. Then read the following article aloud slowly.

The Daytime Sky

What is in the daytime sky?

We can see the sun in the daytime. The sun is really a star. The sun is close to our planet. This makes it seem much brighter and bigger than the other stars we see.

Sometimes you can see clouds in the sky. Clouds are made up of tiny drops of ice or water.

We can see lightning in the sky. Lightning can happen in the day and the night. Lightning is a bright flash of electricity. Lightning happens when drops of ice in a cloud bump into drops of water.

2. Lead a brief class discussion about the article, using the questions below.

    Question 1: What things have you seen in the daytime sky?

    Question 2: What makes lightning?

3. Explain to children that they will use this article and another article to draw a picture and write a report about the sky.

Student Task Overview

Part 1 *(10 minutes)*

Tell children that you will read an article about the sky at night. Then read the following article aloud slowly.

Look Up at Night

What is in the nighttime sky?

You can see the moon at night. The moon does not make its own light. Light from the sun is reflected on the moon, and that is what we see when the moon shines.

Stars are big balls of hot gas. They give off their own light. The sun is the closest star to us. Other stars are bigger than the sun. We can see them only at night because they are very, very far away from us.

The directions for each item are below. Help the children identify the pictures in each row as best as they can. Read the article aloud multiple times if needed.

Item 1: Say: *Listen to the question about the article "The Daytime Sky": What happens when drops of ice in a cloud bump into drops of water?*

clouds

the sun

lightning

Item 2: Say: *Listen to the question about the article "Look Up at Night": What makes the moon shine bright?*

the sun

lightning

clouds

Part 2 *(15 minutes)*

Tell children they will now draw a picture and write a report. Read both articles again. Then read the following question aloud slowly: *Think about the information in the two articles I read, "The Daytime Sky" and "Look Up at Night." What are two things that you read about that you can see in the sky? Tell about one thing from "The Daytime Sky" and one thing from "Look Up at Night." Draw your answer on a sheet of paper. Then write your response.*

Task Specifications and Scoring Rubrics

Tell children that a good response is clear and answers the question.

Ask children to verbally explain their drawings or elaborate on their writing. Take these verbal responses into account as you score children's responses using the Performance Task: Informative Writing Rubric.

Scoring and Interpreting the Results

Scoring

The answers to the Assessments and Performance Tasks can be found in the Answer Keys section. Each correct response to a selected-response item is worth one point. Each constructed-response item is worth two points. Constructed-response items and essay responses should be scored using the rubrics provided in this book. Sample answers to the constructed-response items are given on the Answer Key and should be used as a guide to score a child's responses. Because these questions require children to think deeply about comprehension, both the teacher and children can learn a great deal by discussing children's responses and their reasoning.

Duplicate a Test Record Form for each child and enter the scores in the Student Score column. This form will allow you to track a child's performance across the year. If you require a percentage score for each test to help in assigning grades, apply the formula in the optional Final Score row and record that score.

Interpreting

Consider each child's scores on the Test Record Form. Children who achieve an Acceptable Score (indicated on the form) or higher are most likely ready to move to the next unit in the book.

For struggling children, duplicate the Answer Key. Circle the item numbers answered incorrectly for each Assessment or Performance Task and compare the corresponding skills indicated. Look for patterns among the errors to help you decide which skills need reteaching and more practice.

Assessment 1

Item Number	Correct Answer	Unit, Lesson, Program Skill	CCSS	Depth of Knowledge
		WRITING		
1	See rubric on p. T27.	U1L1: Writing: Narrative	W.K.3	2
	Sample two-point response: Drawing should show something that could be in a park, such as a playground, friends, or an animal. Student may label their drawing or write an answer such as "I like swings."			
	Sample one-point response: Drawing should show something that could be in a park. No writing about drawing is present.			
		LISTENING		
2	C	U1L4: Speaking and Listening: Identify and Interpret Purpose, Central Idea, and Key Points	SL.K.2	1
3	A, C	U1L4: Speaking and Listening: Identify and Interpret Purpose, Central Idea, and Key Points	SL.K.2	2
4	C	U1L4: Speaking and Listening: Identify and Interpret Purpose, Central Idea, and Key Points	SL.K.2	3
5	B	U1L4: Speaking and Listening: Identify and Interpret Purpose, Central Idea, and Key Points	SL.K.2	2
6	B	U1L4: Speaking and Listening: Identify and Interpret Purpose, Central Idea, and Key Points	SL.K.2	2
7	B, C	U1L4: Speaking and Listening: Identify and Interpret Purpose, Central Idea, and Key Points	SL.K.2	3

Performance Task 1

Item Number	Correct Answer	Unit, Lesson, Program Skill	CCSS	Depth of Knowledge
1	B	U2L8: Comprehension: Details	RI.K.1	2
2	A	U1L1: Comprehension: Main Ideas	RI.K.2	1
Essay Response	See rubric on p. T28.	U1L5: Writing: Narrative	W.K.3	3

Assessment 2

Item Number	Correct Answer	Unit, Lesson, Program Skill	CCSS	Depth of Knowledge
		WRITING		
1	See rubric on p. T27.	U2L8: Writing: Informative	W.K.2	2
	Sample two-point response: Drawing should show something that could be in a city, such as a car or a building. Possible writing "We can see a red car."			
	Sample one-point response: Drawing should show something that could be in a city. No writing about drawing is present.			
		LISTENING		
2	C	U2L6: Speaking and Listening: Identify Ideas and Supporting Evidence	SL.K.3	1
3	B	U2L6: Speaking and Listening: Identify Ideas and Supporting Evidence	SL.K.2	2
4	A	U3L12: Speaking and Listening: Draw and Support Conclusions	SL.K.2	2
5	B	U2L6: Speaking and Listening: Identify Ideas and Supporting Evidence	SL.K.3	2
6	B, C	U2L6: Speaking and Listening: Identify Ideas and Supporting Evidence	SL.K.2	2
7	B	U3L12: Speaking and Listening: Draw and Support Conclusions	SL.K.2	3

Performance Task 2

Item Number	Correct Answer	Unit, Lesson, Program Skill	CCSS	Depth of Knowledge
1	dragonfly	U3L11: Comprehension: Compare and Contrast	RI.K.1	1
2	beak	U3L13: Comprehension: Text and Graphic Features	RI.K.7	2
Essay Response	See rubric on p. T30.	U4L20: Writing: Opinion	W.K.1	3

Assessment 3

Item Number	Correct Answer	Unit, Lesson, Program Skill	CCSS	Depth of Knowledge
READING				
1	C	U4L17: Comprehension: Sequence of Events	RI.K.3	1
2	good	U4L18: Comprehension: Author's Purpose	RI.K.8	2
3	B	U5L23: Comprehension: Sequence of Events	RI.K.3	1
4	A	U4L16: Comprehension: Details	RI.K.1	2
5	See rubric on p. T27.	U5L24: Comprehension: Conclusions	RI.K.3	3
	Sample two-point response: Drawing should show the man holding a sign help a child or children cross the street. Possible writing: "He helps them."			
	Sample one-point response: Drawing should show the man holding a sign help a child or children cross the street. No writing about drawing is present.			
6	A	U4L19: Comprehension: Cause and Effect	RL.K.3	2
7	A	U4L20: Comprehension: Sequence of Events	RL.K.3	1
8	C	U5L25: Comprehension: Text and Graphic Features	RL.K.7	2
9	C	U5L21: Comprehension: Details	RL.K.1	2
10	sad	U5L22: Comprehension: Story Structure	RL.K.3	2
WRITING				
11	See rubric on p. T27.	U4L20: Writing: Opinion	W.K.1	2
	Sample two-point response: Drawing should show something that the child thinks is fun. Possible writing: The child may label their drawing or write an answer such as "I like to jump. It is fun."			
	Sample one-point response: Drawing should show something that the child thinks is fun. No writing about drawing is present.			
LISTENING				
12	C	U5L22: Speaking and Listening: Identify and Interpret Purpose, Central Idea, and Key Points	SL.K.2	2
13	B	U5L22: Speaking and Listening: Identify and Interpret Purpose, Central Idea, and Key Points	SL.K.2	1
14	A, C	U4L16: Speaking and Listening: Identify Ideas and Supporting Evidence	SL.K.3	2
15	B	U5L22: Speaking and Listening: Identify and Interpret Purpose, Central Idea, and Key Points	SL.K.2	2
16	A, C	U4L16: Speaking and Listening: Identify Ideas and Supporting Evidence	SL.K.3	1
17	A	U4L16: Speaking and Listening: Identify Ideas and Supporting Evidence	SL.K.3	2

Performance Task 3

Item Number	Correct Answer	Unit, Lesson, Program Skill	CCSS	Depth of Knowledge
1	C	U6L29: Comprehension: Main Idea and Details	RI.K.2	1
2	A	U6L29: Comprehension: Main Idea and Details	RI.K.2	2
Essay Response	See rubric on p. T29.	U5L25: Writing: Informative	W.K.2	3

Constructed-Response Rubrics

READING Rubric

Score of 2	• The drawing and/or writing is organized. • The drawing and/or writing shows that the child was able to understand the text. • The drawing and/or writing includes clear evidence from the text that supports the child's response. • The drawing and/or writing includes specific details that relate to the text.
Score of 1	• The drawing and/or writing may not be organized. • The drawing and/or writing shows that the child may not have clearly understood the text. • The drawing and/or writing includes little evidence from the text that supports the child's response. • The drawing and/or writing includes some details that relate to the text.
Score of 0	• The drawing and/or writing is not organized. • The drawing and/or writing shows that the child did not understand the text. • The drawing and/or writing includes no evidence or details from the text.

WRITING Rubric

Score of 2	• The drawing and/or writing is connected to the prompt. • The drawing and/or writing includes details and/or evidence to support the child's response. • When writing is present, the response includes elaboration and uses specific words.
Score of 1	• The drawing and/or writing is connected to the prompt but may be difficult to understand. • The drawing and/or writing includes details and/or evidence to support the child's response. • When writing is present, the response includes limited elaboration and uses general words.
Score of 0	• The drawing and/or writing has a weak or no connection to the prompt or may repeat information from the prompt. • The drawing and/or writing does not address the task and provides few or no details or evidence. • When writing is present, the response includes no elaboration.

Performance Task: Narrative Writing Rubric

Score	4	3	2	1	NS
Purpose/Organization	**The child creates an effective narrative.** • Plot contains a single event or loosely linked events	**The child creates a generally effective narrative.** • Plot contains events that are generally linked	**The child creates an ineffective narrative.** • Minimal development of plot	**The child has not created a narrative.** • Little or no plot	• Not intelligible • Not written in English • Not on topic
Development/Elaboration	**The narrative includes effective development.** • Links to sources may enrich the narrative • Tells about events in order • Contains a reaction to what happened and a clear ending	**The narrative includes some development.** • Links to sources may contribute to the narrative • Tells about events mostly in order • Contains somewhat of a reaction to what happened or a clear ending	**The narrative includes little or no development.** • Links to sources may be unsuccessful but do not detract from the narrative • Tells about events in random order • Contains no apparent reaction to what happened; ending is abrupt or not on topic	**The narrative does not demonstrate any development.** • Links to sources, if present, may interfere with the narrative • Little or no attempt to order events • Contains no attempt at a reaction or clear ending	• Not intelligible • Not written in English • Not on topic

Score	2	1	0	NS
Conventions	**The response demonstrates adequate development of conventions.** • Some capitalization and punctuation • Knowledge of most sound-letter relationships	**The response demonstrates partial development of conventions.** • Inconsistent capitalization and punctuation • Some knowledge of sound-letter relationships	**The response demonstrates little or no development of conventions.** • Little or no capitalization or punctuation • Little or no knowledge of sound-letter relationships	• Not intelligible • Not written in English • Not on topic

Performance Task: Informative/Explanatory Writing Rubric

Score	4	3	2	1	NS
Purpose/Organization	**The response is effective.** • Main idea is clear • Ideas follow a logical sequence	**The response is generally effective.** • Main idea is clear • Ideas follow an adequate sequence	**The response is mostly ineffective.** • Main idea may be somewhat unclear • Sequence of ideas may be weak or unclear	**The response is wholly ineffective.** • Main idea may be confusing • Sequence of ideas is unorganized	• Not intelligible • Not written in English • Not on topic
Evidence/Elaboration	**The response includes effective elaboration.** • Evidence from sources is integrated, is relevant, and supports key ideas • Provides strong details • Details are clear and appropriate	**The response includes some elaboration.** • Evidence from sources is integrated, is relevant, and adequately supports key ideas • Provides adequate details • Details are mostly appropriate	**The response includes little or no elaboration.** • Evidence from sources may be poorly integrated or irrelevant, or only loosely supports key ideas • Provides weak details • Details are somewhat irrelevant	**The response does not demonstrate any elaboration.** • Evidence from sources, if present, may be irrelevant with little support for key ideas • Provides few details • Details are irrelevant	• Not intelligible • Not written in English • Not on topic

Score	2	1	0	NS
Conventions	**The response demonstrates adequate development of conventions.** • Some capitalization and punctuation • Knowledge of most sound-letter relationships	**The response demonstrates partial development of conventions.** • Inconsistent capitalization and punctuation • Some knowledge of sound-letter relationships	**The response demonstrates little or no development of conventions.** • Little or no capitalization or punctuation • Little or no knowledge of sound-letter relationships	• Not intelligible • Not written in English • Not on topic

Performance Task: Opinion Writing Rubric

Score	4	3	2	1	NS
Purpose/Organization	The response is effective. • Opinion is clear • Ideas follow a logical sequence	The response is generally effective. • Opinion is clear • Ideas follow an adequate sequence	The response is mostly ineffective. • Opinion may be somewhat unclear • Sequence of ideas may be weak or unclear	The response is wholly ineffective. • Opinion may be confusing • Sequence of ideas is unorganized	• Not intelligible • Not written in English • Not on topic
Evidence/Elaboration	The response includes effective support and elaboration. • Evidence from sources is relevant, and supports key ideas • Provides strong evidence • Details are clear and appropriate	The response includes some support and elaboration. • Evidence from sources is integrated, is relevant, and adequately supports key ideas • Provides adequate evidence • Details are mostly appropriate	The response includes little or no support or elaboration. • Evidence from sources may be poorly integrated or irrelevant, or only loosely supports key ideas • Provides weak evidence • Details are somewhat irrelevant	The response does not demonstrate any support or elaboration. • Evidence from sources, if present, may be irrelevant with little support for key ideas • Provides little or no evidence • Details are irrelevant	• Not intelligible • Not written in English • Not on topic

Score	2	1	0	NS
Conventions	The response demonstrates adequate development of conventions. • Some capitalization and punctuation • Knowledge of most sound-letter relationships	The response demonstrates partial development of conventions. • Inconsistent capitalization and punctuation • Some knowledge of sound-letter relationships	The response demonstrates little or no development of conventions. • Little or no capitalization or punctuation • Little or no knowledge of sound-letter relationships	• Not intelligible • Not written in English • Not on topic

Test Record Form

Student Name _____

Assessment 1

Date _____

Date Administered _____		Possible Score	Acceptable Score	Student Score
Writing (Item 1)*	Constructed-Response	2	1	
Listening (Items 2–7)		6	5	
	Total	8	6	
FINAL SCORE = Total Student Score x 12.5 = _____				

Performance Task 1

Date _____

Date Administered _____	Possible Score	Acceptable Score	Student Score
Part 1 (Items 1–2)*	3	2	
Part 2 (Essay Response)	10	7	
Total	13	9	
FINAL SCORE = Total Student Score x 11.11 = _____			

Assessment 2

Date _____

Date Administered _____		Possible Score	Acceptable Score	Student Score
Writing (Item 1)*	Constructed-Response	2	1	
Listening (Items 2–7)		6	5	
	Total	8	6	
FINAL SCORE = Total Student Score x 12.5 = _____				

Performance Task 2

Date _____

Date Administered _____	Possible Score	Acceptable Score	Student Score
Part 1 (Items 1–2)*	3	2	
Part 2 (Essay Response)	10	7	
Total	13	9	
FINAL SCORE = Total Student Score x 11.11 = _____			

Assessment 3

Date _____

Date Administered _____		Possible Score	Acceptable Score	Student Score
Reading (Items 1–10)*	Selected-Response	9	7	
	Constructed-Response	2		
Writing (Item 11)*	Constructed-Response	2	1	
Listening (Items 12–17)		6	5	
	Total	19	13	
FINAL SCORE = Total Student Score x 5.26 = _____				

Performance Task 3

Date _____

Date Administered _____	Possible Score	Acceptable Score	Student Score
Part 1 (Items 1–2)*	3	2	
Part 2 (Essay Response)	10	7	
Total	13	9	
FINAL SCORE = Total Student Score x 11.11 = _____			

*This section includes constructed-response items worth up to two points each. Please note when scoring.

Name _____ Date _____

Assessment 1
Writing

I Like the Park

I like the _____ .

I like the _____ .

I like the _____ .

I like the  .

1

Name _____ Date _____

Name _____ Date _____

Listening

Amazing Spiders

3

Name _____ Date _____

② 2 4 8

---

③

---

④

What Are Insects Good For?

5

6
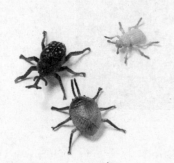  

7

Performance Task 1
Part 1

Everyone Can Help

Trucks

1

2

 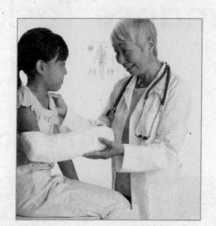 

Name _____ Date _____

Part 2

Assessment 2
Writing

What Can You See in a City?

We can see a _____ .

We can see a _____ .

We can see a _____ .

Name _____ Date _____

We can see a _____.

We can see a _____.

We can see a _____.

12

Name _____ Date _____

1

Name _____ Date _____

Listening

What Makes a Snowflake

Name _____ Date _____

2

3

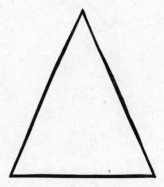  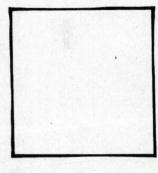

4

Name _____ Date _____

Winter Fun

Name _____ Date _____

5

6

7

17

Performance Task 2
Part 1

Bugs, Bugs, Bugs

Feathered Friends

Name _____ Date _____

1

2

Name _____ Date _____

Part 2

Assessment 3
Reading

We Can Help

We can help.

It is good to help.

It can be fun.

She can help.

She can help him hit a ball.

See how he can help?

He can help Pam go!

See how a kid can help?

He can jog with the dog.

A big kid can help.

He can help his dad.

See how a dad and kid can help?

We can all help.

Then we can play with a pal.

It is good to help!

Name _____ • Date _____

1 help Pam go

jog with a dog

play with a pal

---

2 We can all help.

Then we can play with a pal.

It is good to help!

Name _____ Date _____

We Go to School

We are here.

We sit with her.

It is fun!

We can get help.

She can help!

Name _____ Date _____

We can help.

We help the pets.

We get them food.

See what we make?

Then we all play tag.

Now we can go!

This man can help.

See how he can help her?

3 They go.

They sit.

They play.

---

4 pets

kids

the man

5

_____
- -
_____

_____
- -
_____

_____
- -
_____

The Tree

I am Tom.

We got a tree.

We help dig.

We dig and dig.

The tree is not in the pot.

It will get big.

See what it has on it now?

Name _____ Date _____

See what it has on it?

See the tree now?

It has plums on it.

Soon the plums will get big.

Now the tree is big.

Now the plums are big.

It is time to have plums!

Name _____ Date _____

6 He got a tree.

They dig and dig.

The tree is not in the pot.

---

7 We got plums.

The tree got big.

We put the tree in a pot.

8

 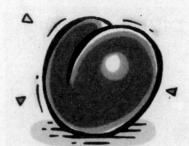 

Name _____ Date _____

Bob Dog and Pat Cat

Bob Dog was sad.

I want to play.

I see a cat!

Bob Dog met Pat Cat.

I can play with Pat Cat!

Bob Dog hid.

Then Pat Cat hid.

Name _____ Date _____

Bob Dog cannot see Pat Cat.

Where is Pat Cat?

Is she up the tree?

No!

Tap, tap, tap.

Where is Pat Cat?

Here is Pat Cat!

We can play now.

We have fun!

9 Pat is a dog.

Pat is up the tree.

He cannot see Pat.

---

10 Bob Dog was sad.

I want to play.

I see a cat!

Writing

What I Like

I can play a game.

I like to play.

It is fun!

Name _____ Date _____

I can go on a bus.

I like to go on a bus.

The bus is fun!

This is my big dog.

She is a good dog!

She is fun!

Name _____ Date _____

11

[drawing box]

_____

- - - - - - - - - - - - - - - - - - - -

_____

_____

- - - - - - - - - - - - - - - - - - - -

_____

_____

- - - - - - - - - - - - - - - - - - - -

_____

Name _____ Date _____

Listening

Moon Shapes

Name _____ Date _____

 12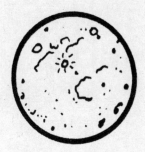

13

14

Summer

Name _____ Date _____

15

16

17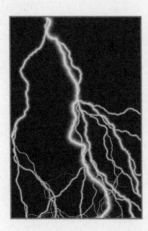

Performance Task 3
Overview

The Daytime Sky

Look Up at Night

Name _____ Date _____

Part 1

---

②

Name _____ Date _____

Part 2

Name _____ Date _____